C000088721

...ion
...gs
...eed
...d
...tter!
CHAMPAGNE
chocolate...

>N.B. - Grass seed & assorted plants.
* MAKE ~~appt~~ *
* HAIR APPOINTMENT!

Get HOLIDAY BROCHURES!!

new suite.   - passport.
fast car.   - travellers'
                      cheques
Clothes / suitcase(s)
Bikini   toothbrush.

The
SECRET
THOUGHTS
of
WOMEN

Artwork assistance on all six
books ~ Andrew Liney

First published in 1996

Copyright Steven Appleby © 1996

The moral right of the author
has been asserted blah blah...

Bloomsbury Publishing PLC
2 Soho Square, London W1V 6HB

ISBN 0 7475 2968 X

Printed in Great Britain by
St. Edmundsbury Press, Suffolk

MANY THANKS TO:

Abigail; Gill; Janny; Jean; Jessamy; Karen; Kate; Linda; Liz; Lorna; Mary; Nicola; Noni; Rachel; Ros & Sophie.

AGE 20

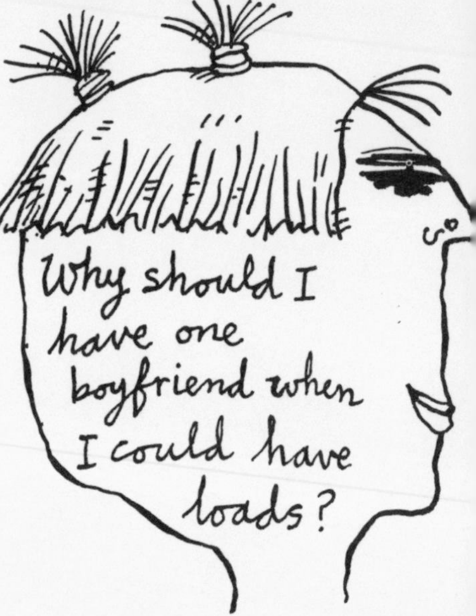

Your new baby? How GORGEOUS... SWEET... DARLING...
My God, he looks like a monkey!

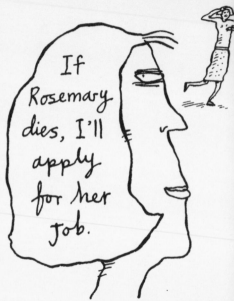

As soon as someone leaves the room I'm going to talk about them.
The loo? Top of the stairs on the right.

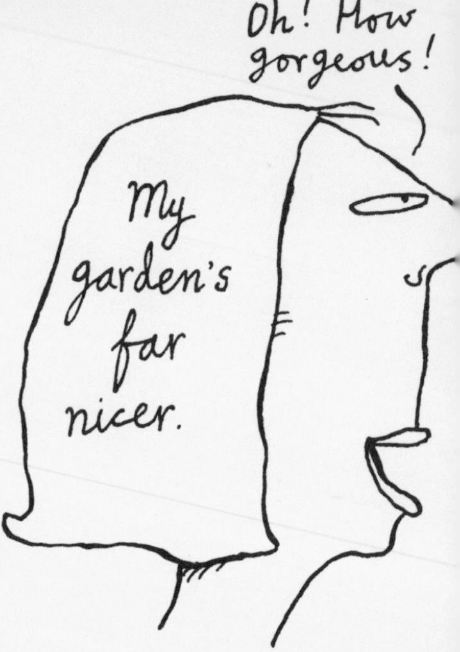
Oh! How gorgeous!
My garden's far nicer.

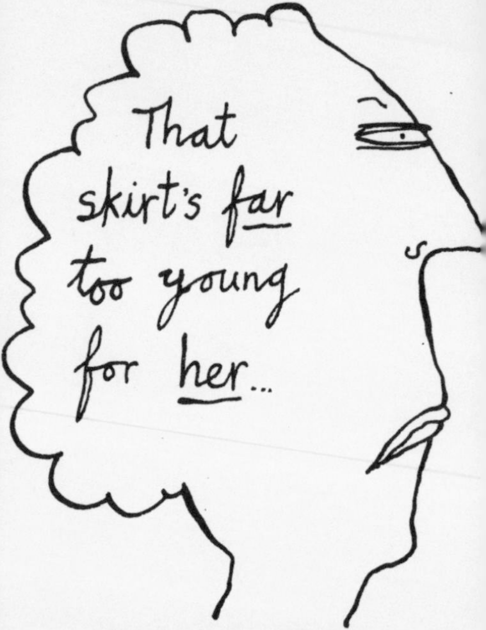
That skirt's far too young for her...

And she's _wearing_ so much make-up she looks like a transvestite.

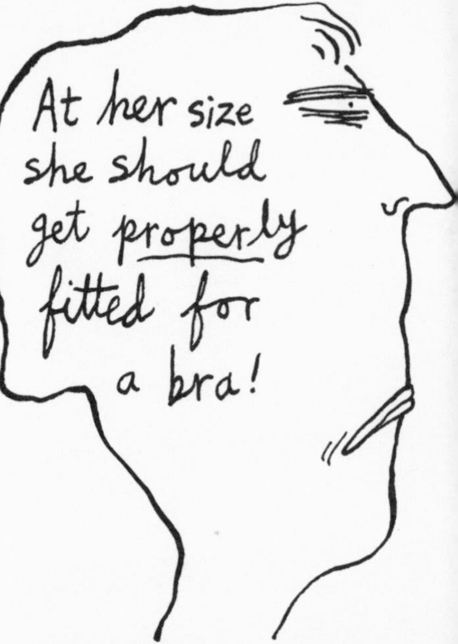
At her size she should get properly fitted for a bra!

I can't imagine what it would be like to have sex with an animal...

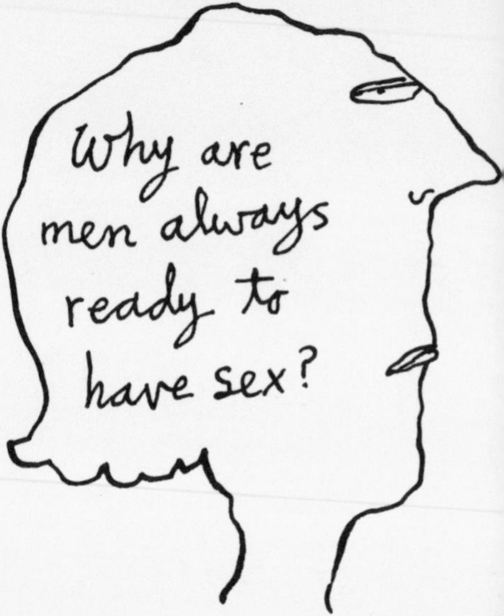
Why are
men always
ready to
have sex?

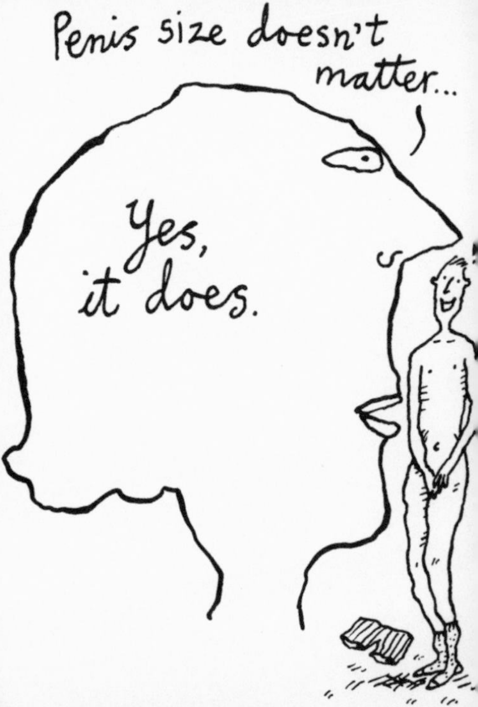
Penis size doesn't matter...
Yes, it does.

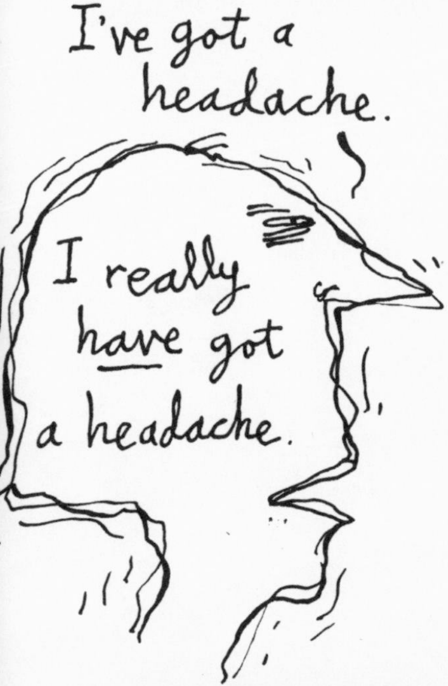
I've got a headache.
I really have got a headache.

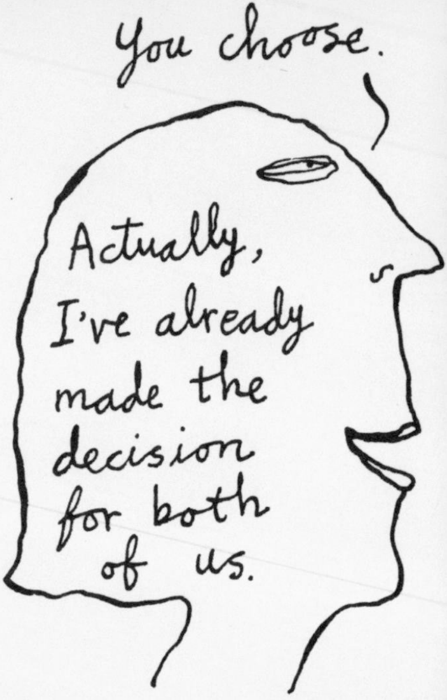
You choose.
Actually, I've already made the decision for both of us.

I've got PMT.
I'm going to disagree with whatever you say and blame it on my hormones.

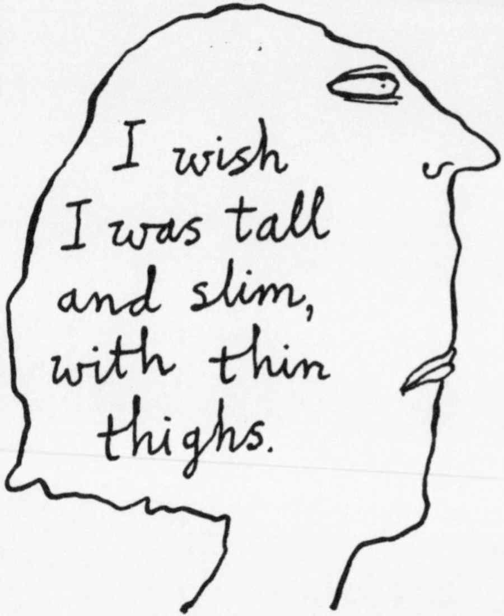
I wish
I was tall
and slim,
with thin
thighs.

When we're married I'll...
Live happily ever after?
...make some changes round here!

After we're married.
I can pass wind and stop bothering to shave my legs.

A THOUGHT TOO
EMBARRASSING TO
SPEAK ALOUD:

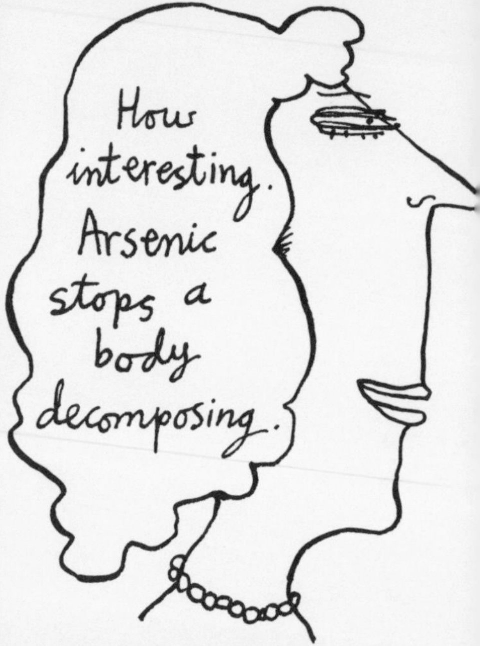
How interesting. Arsenic stops a body decomposing.

I wonder why there are few women serial killers?
Perhaps we don't get caught.

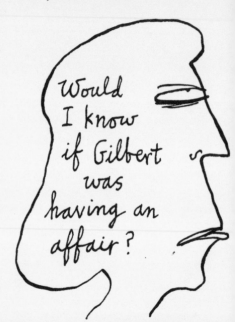

Would I know if Gilbert was having an affair?

SOME OBSERVATIONS LEADING TO ONLY ONE CONCLUSION:

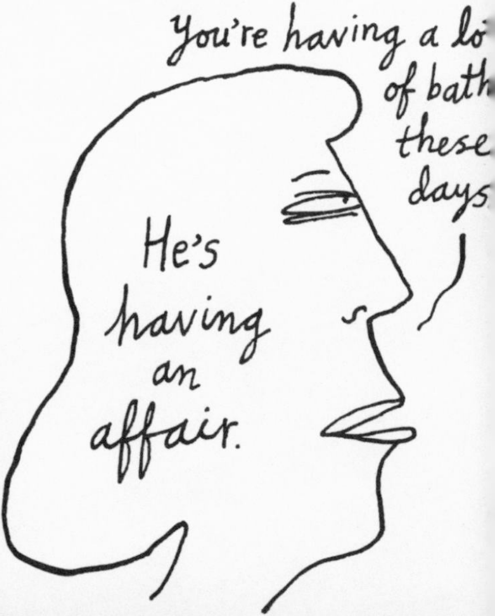

We've had loads of wrong numbers recently
He's having an affair.

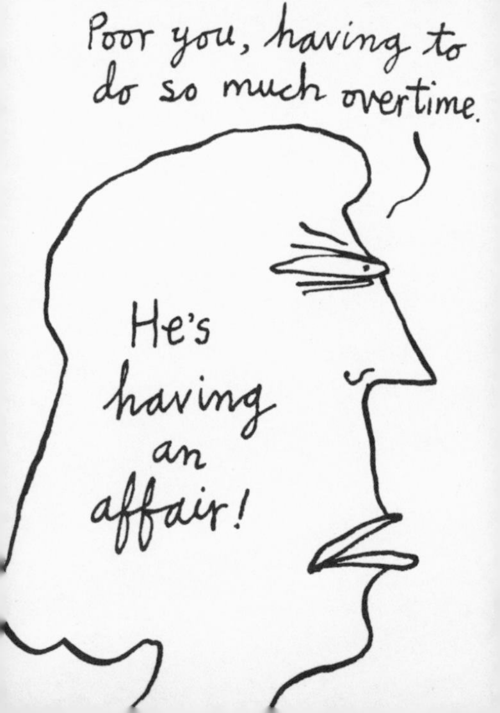
Poor you, having to do so much overtime.
He's having an affair!

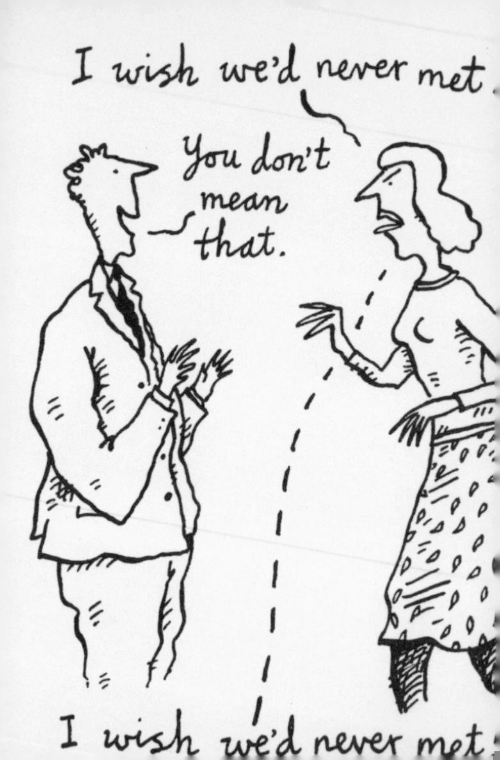
I wish we'd never met
You don't mean that.
I wish we'd never met

What are you thinking about?
A world without men.
Oh... this and that.

Have a good day, dear.
I should have married *
* Anyone else but you.

Only a man could think women suffer from penis envy

Sometimes I wish I <u>could</u> have a willie for a week or two — just to try it out.

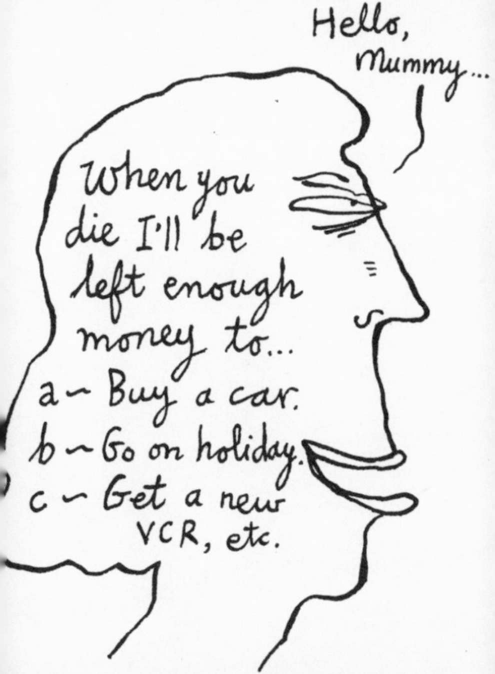
Hello, Mummy...
When you die I'll be left enough money to...
a – Buy a car.
b – Go on holiday.
c – Get a new VCR, etc.

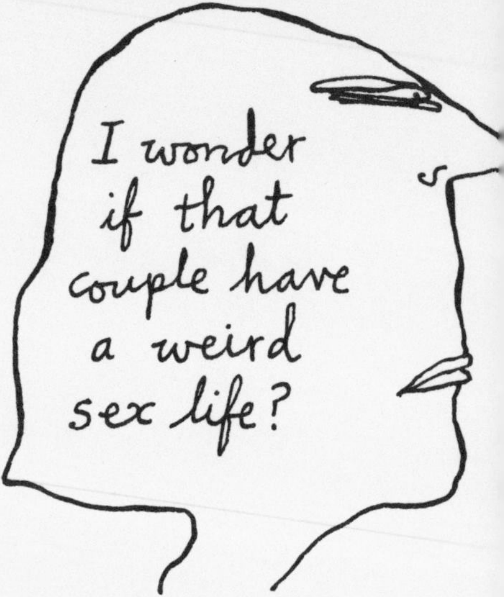
I wonder
if that
couple have
a weird
sex life?

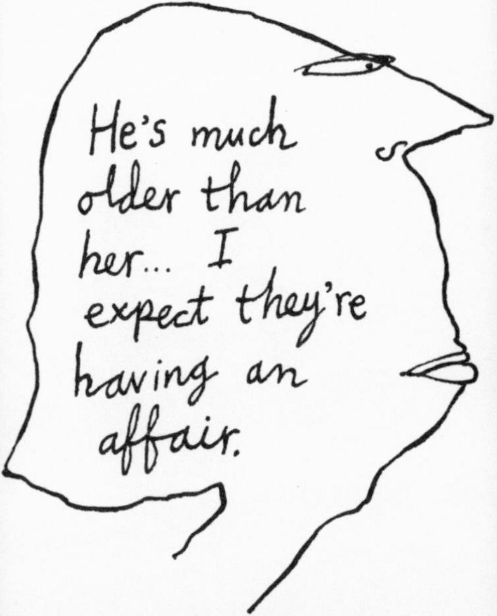
He's much older than her... I expect they're having an affair.

Sex choc
sex choc sex
choc sex choc
sex choc sex
choc sex choc
sex choc...

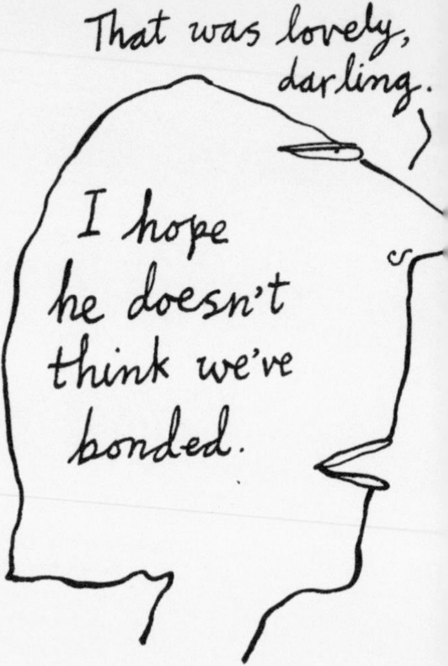
That was lovely, darling.
I hope he doesn't think we've bonded.

Meet Roger. He's really sensitive. A new man.
Hi.
You lucky thing, Fiona.
Hi, Roger.
Tosser!

See you later. Hope I manage.
You'll be fine.
I'll ring up every 15 minutes, because men can't be trusted.

I wish
the children
fighting and
being horrible
weren't mine...

And that mine were the ones doing the colouring-in.

Jim's a few hours late home – I hope he's okay...
Maybe he's been killed by a maniac on the street. That would get me out of this relationship and solve my money worries...

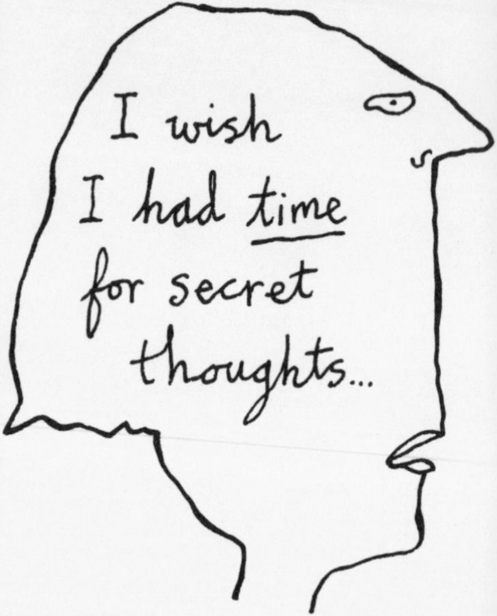
I wish
I had time
for secret
thoughts...

W/up liquid.   Persil/c

CHOC!   toilet cleaner   Ho

Sugar   tampons

Bread   nappies   Bath sponge

butter

flour. .

crisps

                    (c

veg: crisps

carrots, peas   cereals

potatoes/new   baby food

leeks

tomatoes   arsenic

lettuce   sharp knives

s. onions

cucumber   polythene

                    sheeting

                    spade